M. L. Jordan briefly lived on a farm in Perryville, Kentucky close to the Perryville Battlefield. She holds a BA in religious studies from Centre College and is also a graduate of Midway College of Nursing. She was an RN for many years working mainly in the emergency room and as a hospice nurse. She and her husband live on the coast in South Carolina.

For my daughter, Sarah

I have a small daughter called Cleis, who is like a golden
flower
I wouldn't take all Croesus' kingdom with love thrown in,
for her

Sappho

M. L. Jordan

THE CHAPLIN RIVER LETTERS

AUSTIN MACAULEY PUBLISHERS™

LONDON • CAMBRIDGE • NEW YORK • SHARJAH

Ordering Information
Quantity sales: Special discounts are available on quantity purchases by corporations, associations, and others. For details, contact the publisher at the address below.

Publisher's Cataloging-in-Publication data
Jordan, M.L.
The Chaplin River Letters

ISBN 9798889104971 (Paperback)
ISBN 9798889104988 (Hardback)
ISBN 9798889104995 (ePub e-book)

Library of Congress Control Number: 2023918297

www.austinmacauley.com/us

First Published 2024
Austin Macauley Publishers LLC
40 Wall Street, 33rd Floor, Suite 3302
New York, NY 10005
USA

mail-usa@austinmacauley.com
+1 (646) 5125767

My husband, Tom, a biblical scholar and archaeologist, encouraged me to write this little book.

Agatha Christie wrote that an archaeologist is the best husband any woman could have because the older she gets the more interested he is in her.

Prologue

Of all the letters, diaries, journals, and first-hand accounts about the Civil War that made it into the history books, redacted to give the most sterilized version of accounts witnessed by the actual people who lived the experience, letters recently found on the banks of the Chaplin River in central Kentucky can only be described as staggering, pulsing with the very thing many of the soldiers were robbed of—life. Sermons were posted in newspapers as editors, North and South, sanctioned bloodshed while using the Bible to endorse war. Like Joshua's trumpet, many voices blasted their truth, convinced their cause was righteous as brother killed brother.

Some, however, were not so ready and willing to become cannon fodder. One soldier writes home asking if he's a coward because he just wants to slip away and return home and take his family west. Mothers wrote sons begging them to "not make a show of bravery" but to protect themselves at all costs, while one wife makes us blush in her longing for her husband.

Found in a satchel on property near the Perryville Battlefield in Perryville, Kentucky, the letters were discovered beneath a deer blind on the bluffs above the

Chaplin River. Rumors circulated for many years, according to old-timers, who spoke of an old Indian who used to live in the caves at the place "where the herons nest" and his mutterings about buried bodies They said he often talked about the spot where his great-grandfather had buried young soldiers after the battle of Perryville, describing a large field surrounded on three sides by the Chaplin, where it made a horseshoe bend in the river. It was in this field where a large stand of sycamores and cedars stood sentinel.

Indeed, it would turn out to be the final resting place where a large stone was placed to mark the graves. The marker, upturned and laying on its side, had no inscription to indicate that this was hallowed ground, the forgotten overgrown with lichen and moss, and the dust of leaves long dead above, the dust of flesh and bone below. It was here that local hunters erected a deer blind, its use long ago abandoned.

A professor, Shepherd Watkins, and his wife Cleo lived nearby. The entire length of one side of their five acres ran beside the Chaplin River. Daily they walked their dogs on neighboring property to a heron rookery, the nests high in the tall sycamores above the gentle flowing Chaplin. Shep and Cleo would often stop along the route at the stand of trees in the middle of a field to let the dogs sniff and do what dogs do as they peered into the area beneath an old deer blind. A discarded tractor tire lay tangled in the muck littered with broken beer bottles and rusty tins of tobacco. The site also became a refuse pile for a weathered and dirty lawn chair which lay crumpled in the weeds, together with remnants of torn fencing and old stones pilfered from a rock wall, used to encircle what was once an old campfire. It was here they found a stone marker.

Taking some time off after working as a hospice nurse to gift herself with a mental health break after the daily toll of such sad but important work, Cleo cast about for something useful she could do in the meantime to keep her occupied. She began work as a docent at the Perryville Battlefield Museum for a season where she learned a great deal about the area as well as the battle. It was there that Cleo first heard the rumors about the bodies and the cave and the old Indian.

Cleo knew space and geography and how hills fell away to streams that flowed by meadows that heaved again toward mountains. She had the gift of going to a place once, by car or on foot, having never been there before and was able to retrace her route without giving it too much thought, even if separated by days or weeks or years. She took it for granted that all people were this way, until she met Shep. They met on an excavation in Israel in the Galilee. Later she would laugh because her archaeologist husband could not find his way to the corner grocery. And he marveled at her gift. So when Cleo heard the Indian story her pulse quickened as she had only been half paying attention when the details were being shared with a Civil War buff who was a local. Jim was regaling a visitor from New Jersey, a re-enactor who was trying to tour all of the Civil War sites before he died.

Cleo had heard so many different stories in the short time she'd been there, she was grateful for Jim who would show up once a week and spend hours talking to visitors. Not only did they learn a lot but so did Cleo. Jim was a fixture in the park and everyone accepted his unofficial status as a park employee. He truly knew as much or more about the park and the Battle of Perryville with the possible exception of the director. And so one day, as he was describing the drought that fateful October day, the old farm house that became a field hospital and Doctor's Creek, dry as a bone, he was interrupted with a question Cleo hadn't heard before. The Re-enactor asked, "Were there any Indian in the area?" Cleo's ears perked up. This was something new.

Jim nodded enthusiastically and explained that there was an old Indian who had stories about a stone marker under a stand of trees in the middle of the field where bodies were buried. He could not remember if it was two or three bodies. Most folks he talked to said two. Cleo grew very still listening to every word, a puzzle coming together. She knew! Shep and Cleo walked by that stand of trees and on to the cave and the rookery above the river thousands of times.

Later that evening, Cleo came up with an idea. She had the skills needed to drop a shallow probe into the ground, using her archaeology training. She had the knowledge, the tools and, most important, the time. With her trowel and pickaxe, Cleo set out early on a beautiful summer day to see what she could find, smiling to herself, thinking there had to be some benefit to being an archaeologist's wife.

It did not take her long to find what she was looking for, two bodies not three were entwined in the rich, damp Kentucky soil. And buried beneath the larger of the two bodies was a mail satchel with the initials "CSA" embossed into a faint outline in the leather. As she held the satchel in her hands she had no idea that the contents would turn out to be something more valuable than gold.

A scapula, later determined to be that of a young male, had been splintered by a terrific force and forensics later concluded it was the destruction of bone undoubtedly caused by a mini-ball. The strap of the satchel was found draped over the shattered bone, flesh long decayed, a few small remnants of cloth, leather, and buckles, laying over bone, with sour notes of human flesh long dead still clinging to what remained. The bodies were carefully removed, along with the satchel, to a nearby college in Danville, Kentucky, for forensic analysis.

While the bodies received the solemn and careful attention they deserved, it would be the satchel's contents that would make a country stand still for a brief moment in time to contemplate the one war that continues to haunt its citizens from that time to this. In their entirety, these remnants of lives just passing through history are remarkable for their wisdom, humor and longing and, as King Solomon reminded, that there is nothing new under the sun.

A note about the letters: In most cases, the letters were found inside envelopes from which postmarks were successfully established indicating points of origin of the writer and thus have been indicated at the top of each letter. Some include dates, others do not. Also, most letters found were singular, one-off letters, with the exception of a few that were found bundled together. Were they perhaps retrieved from the boy whose mother warned him not to make a show of bravery? We can only wonder at the mystery. Finally, all letters were written on or before the Battle of Perryville, October 1862.

Fittingly, one letter's haunting curse stands out for its prescience and the cauldron that is the human heart when stirred with the poisons of war. Discover for yourself. Read and be amazed.

Lexington, KY
September, 1862

Dear James,

I hope this letter finds you in good spirits and well. I have some good news on those horses we looked into purchasing from Pleasant Hill. First, we were so busy concerning ourselves with the horses we forgot to look at their hogs and sheep. These Shaker folks have got quite a community going on south of us that is the envy of any livestock in these parts. When you come home, we need to go back and learn and thing or two from these good men and women. I know their religion says we won't be here too long, but if it's all the same, I'd bet we'll be here for a good long while and there's money to be made from the horses they raise on this Kentucky rye.

I can't see this war business lasting too long. It's got to come to an end sooner rather than later. On that note I'd also like to tell you I've made some solid investments in that distillery over in Frankfort, Buffalo Trace. I aim to turn our name into something while we're here and I'm depending on you to come home and pick up where we left off. Prices are going higher and higher by the day, so I wanted to invest in those things I have a good hunch we will always be in need of down the road. Bourbon and horses, son. I think that's our future. Remember to write your mother. She sees ghosts everywhere and her fears are those of a woman. I have no such problem. You will come home. Believe that and it will be so.

Your loving father,
A. Gaines

Bardstown, KY
July 30, 1862

Dear Mary,

I am holed up in a town as pretty as I've ever seen. If we hadn't worked so hard to lay down roots in Texas, I swear if I were a younger man, I'd say we might want to consider starting our lives back here in Kentucky. I know you beg me to take you back to 254 Talleyrand, but I'm sure if you saw this place, you might change your mind. Oh, to see your sweet smile and those beautiful brown eyes.

After Ft. Donelson and Ft. Henry, this war doesn't stand much of a chance. Unconditional Surrender Grant will be a force to be reckoned with. I don't have a good feeling about our outcome. I am here out of a sense of duty to the South but cannot endure slavery or states' rights or loyalty to Jeff Davis (for all his encouraging slavery in the western territories). I have a long memory and it pains me at times that I ride for the South, but I am with Texas. Our hope will be Lee. You will remember when I took those government supplies and was headed to Fort Belknap. Turns out most of those men I met on that trip are now engaged in this battle, not all on the same side either. Lee, Johnson, Hood—I hope make it safely through this conflict. Fine men, all. It gives me hope that Lee is with the South. If any man's a match for Grant, Lee is that man.

When this war is done, the question that started this mess will finally be settled. I am not comfortable with ownership. After the Kickapoo took our Tommy, I am more convinced than ever that slavery as an institution is wrong. Having him found and returned to us was the work of the

Hand of God, which surely covers all his children, including the black race. I wake every day with a heavy burden on my heart. Perhaps you can relieve me of it?

My hand starts to shake as I write because my heart is so full of longing for you. If there be light at the end of this for us, it's that we value one thing above all, that God created us man and woman, not rich or poor, black or white. We are created in His image. We are his children and the sheep of His pasture.

A few details: I am staying at the Old Talbott Tavern. There's a valley near here that's as pretty as anything I've seen with a little river running through it, Beech Fork. I wish you could see it. There's a drought up here. Hot as Texas. I think we're headed east. If there's any battle to be fought in this country and I meet my end please know that I am happy to die in such a beautiful place. But don't worry, I promised you I'd come home and I am a man of my word. And God's. Health Good.

Your loving husband,
A. McRae Dechman

Springfield, KY
September 1862

Dear Sarah,

How are you, Mallory, Ethan? I am crazed with fright at the news today. I saw a newspaper that was passed around camp from Louisville. It showed a picture of the battle at Antietam and I have to admit I'm more scared than I ever was. You and the kids are not too far away and I could easily make my way home. Honestly, after the pictures I've seen, I'd have to be crazy to want to end up... well, I'll save the details for when I am home. Suffice it to say we can pack and go out west. Everyone is headed that way and we can leave this scourge behind and make a new life. Maybe even go to Mexico.

Whatever you do, don't be surprised if you see me shortly. I can't throw my life away on the battlefield, I have to have hope. You are my hope, and my children are my future. I fear I am not a man who can give myself over to something some politicians have decided I must do because they made rules that I had no hand in making. I am confused, scared and can think of one thing only. Saving myself and you and our family. I cannot be fodder. My children will not grow up without their father.

My misery and doubt confound me. I am so afraid. Can you love a coward? I will fight drought, weather, raging rivers, cold, sickness, but I cannot fight against my brother. What is wrong with this world? I am on my way...

Please love me still,
James

Perryville, KY
September 30, 1862

Dear Clif,

I heard from your mother. Susan told me that you, Candice, and Hannah are bound for Memphis and possibly points farther west. I think this is a good plan. Lord only knows after Bull Run, the second time they fought a battle there, the Yanks have blood lust in their veins and they will no doubt try to seek vengeance. Our boys gave them hell to pay after Seven Pines and I expect there's a tally everyone's keeping on both sides so they can settle some scores. If it were only a game.

Which it clearly is not and therefore, I agree with the decision to move your family as far west as you can. I am not budging one inch from this ground. I have lived my entire life on these bluffs overlooking the Chaplin and I'll be damned if I'm going out looking for trouble. But trouble seems to have found me. The woods are crawling with cavalry, soldiers on march. The sky glows at night with campfire light and the smoke from the burning embers is sweet today but tomorrow will the fires of hell rage in these gracious meadows? I know a cave nearby I will go and hide in when I hear the first crack of a rifle. From what I've seen the canon fire will be heard as far away as Danville to the east and Springfield to the west. Who would have ever thought Perryville, Kentucky would dance with the devil and have her sons and daughters play a part in a grotesque display of man's inhumanity to man?

I am at a loss.   If I die, I have died with peace of mind. I have owned no man.

If I live to see what's on the other side of this matter, I will come to visit you wherever you land, if it is to be.

Your faithful uncle,

Allan

Sewanee, TN
August 31, 1862

My dearest husband,

I know it has not been a month since you left our home and our bed.

I cannot sleep at night. This last week the air is too hot and stifles me so. I feel I cannot think on much else except you. The memory of your touch is so sweet, yet causes me much heartache at the same time.

I find I cannot tend to matters as I need to. I take to my bed a lot, always with thoughts of you.

I feel so tired and heavy. Ma tells me to occupy my time with chores to keep my mind still—not to daydream the hours away however much I long for you. But when I weed, I think of you. I cook and mend and think on you. I move cows from one pasture to another and think only of you. So this week the garden is overgrown, the food burned, my dress unhemmed, and the cows are in three counties.

Sure will be glad when this war is over. The only cause you got is right here in my arms. All else can go to the Devil! The only one to scratch this itch is you.

Your loving wife,
Clara

New Orleans
September 7, 1862

My dear boy,

I write under the greatest duress. My exertions at this effort far exceed my willingness to do so, as I impart terrible news. Evangeline has run off with another man.

Though it grieves me mightily to lay such news at the feet of my brave Confederate soldier, it is news nonetheless that comes as no great surprise to me.

I told you when you married this girl, her Creole blood would rise to the top one day to our disgrace and that day has surely come.

Evidently, she could control her virtue no longer and was rumored to be working Bourbon Street. I did my best to dismiss this talk as idle chatter but was quickly enlightened about the truth of the matter by your own brother, Jacques, who informed me that she has been had by the many rascals of the city. After they used her she was thrown out into the streets where she was finally taken in by the Sisters of Charity. No sooner was she under their gentle and loving care than she was found with the stable master and the two were cast out and where they are now is anybody's guess.

You are well rid of her. The war peels back all our skins to reveal our true selves. Hers was bitter fruit.

We will speak no more of her or this business. Wipe the dust off your feet.

Your loving mother, forever

Charleston, South Carolina
September 6, 1862

Dear Fred,

Well, Ned got back with his leg shot off just like you said. Your brother has tried to be very brave but the pain is writ all over his face.

Because of his needs, I had to have him move in here with us. The kids like having him around. Guess he reminds them of you. I confess I felt the same way at first—forgot what it was like to have a man around the place even if he is a cripple.

Which leads me to some unpleasant news. Ned and I have fallen in love. I can't really explain how or why, exceptin' the obvious—he's here and you ain't.

Now, I know what you're thinking. What good is a cripple to a woman and three kids? Well, since Ned's been here, it's about to be four, and from the size of my belly it could be more. We do have a tendency to spit 'em out two at a time on my father's side. He was a twin after all. And, obviously, you and Ned.

Anyway, I thought you'd best be told before you come back—if you come back. As sorry as I am to break the news to you, I'd be a sight sorrier if you was kilt. I did love you once. And, of course your young'uns still love you and your Ma. Well, Ned too, I 'xpect.

I am sorry,
Kindly,
Stella

P.S.

If you do come back, there's still lots of pretty girls on the Battery. You'd get yourself a new wife right quick.

Nashville, TN
August 9, 1862

Dear Abe,

Just wanted you to know that I had your sister down by the tracks last week…along with three other boys from the neighborhood. She was a might tart by the time it was my turn. What a shame you don't have any more little sisters. But, that's okay. We rounded up your little brothers, Mark and Michael. I know you're thinking they're so young but that's the beauty of it—what better age to get truly acquainted with the women of the world than when you're just becoming a man? Anyhow, we took it upon ourselves to enliven their education in that department.

You remember the whorehouse on the river? Well, your brothers officially joined the club of manhood with some of the finest and most talented beauties Nashville had to offer. In fact, from what I hear, they've been back and time or two.

Although, I must confess, I did hear that Mark, maybe it was Michael, has come down with something since and rumors are swirling that it's the clap. I do feel right poorly about that.

So, that's all the news from home. And, oh yes, by the way, you can kiss my ass, you sorry piece of shit. This is payback for that stunt you pulled with my best mare!

Jonathan

P.S.

There's a special place in hell for a man who would do what you did with that horse!

Harrodsburg, KY
September 8, 1862

Dear Joe,

You won't believe what we got in the camp today. Our troops picked up a few bawdy ladies from Louisville two weeks back. Some of the boys had been passin' 'em off as soldiers—given 'em clothes and they had their hair all tucked up under their kepi so's you'd just think it was a little 'ol boy and no girl. They was found out when two of 'em were in the cot—makin' all kinds of rackit. He's now in the stockade and the women—they found two more in disguise— were returned to Louisville under guard.

Ever since Shiloh, there have been a lot of women showing up in the ranks. Sometimes it seems like every other cot has a woman hidin' under a blanket. And if the clap serves as any proof of women being in the camp, it sure ain't slowed nobody down.

I knew I was going to see things I ain't never seen before but I sure was not expecting to see this kind of behavior in the ranks. I heard war was hell—but this is worse. It is Sodom and Gomora.

Please say a rosary for me. This son of Boston is saving hisself for marriage. I swear by all I hold dear and on the Bible Daddy gave me that I read every night before I close my eyes.

Your brother,
Phinneas

Cairo, Illinois
July, 1862

Dear Gottfried,

Your father finally arrived but you will not believe the story I am about to tell you. So much confusion!

Somehow he ended up in Frankfort, which, it turns out is a town in Kentucky. When he realized the mistake—explaining he was from Frankfort, Germany, and trying to get to Cairo, Illinois, not Cairo, Egypt, he'd already been on a train headed east. He realized his mistake when he went from Versailles to Paris. He kept trying to tell people he was going the wrong way but his English is so bad they kept thinking he was trying to go back home. He said he spent three days traveling all over Kentucky and every place he went was the name of someplace else. At one point, he saw a sign to Palestine but not the one you think!

I tell you it's no wonder these people are at war—they don't have their own identity. I don't know why they care so much about the differences between blacks and whites. Here a white man is from Cairo and a black man is from Frankfort! Is it me or is the rest of the world crazy? Are we sure we want to stay in this country?

Dumkoffs—all of them.

So, I have sent you some sausages—hope they didn't spoil. Write soon. Practice your English.

Ich liebe dich
Mama

September, 1962

Dear George,

It is my sad duty to inform you that your brother Joseph was kicked in the head by a mule while trying to shod the beast early this morning. The farrier on shift was drunk, and I expect, knowing Joseph, he thought he could do the job as well as any grown man. Guess there's few things a 12-year-old boy won't try.

He struggled throughout the day. His breathing grew more and more labored and he finally gave up the ghost around three o'clock. I suppose that's as good as any time to die—maybe the best—after all, Our Lord and Savior Jesus Christ died at three. Maybe that will be some comfort to you.

He was the best snare drummer we ever had. And there's no one to take his place. The child tried to be a help in all ways, to his credit.

Please break the news to your Ma. I did not have the heart to write her directly. After having to send you home with both legs shot off, this last news had best come from you.

You are all she has left after Shiloh. May God give you peace. Your brother is buried in an old churchyard near a place called Springfield, Kentucky.

Your obt. Servant,

Bragg

Perryville, Kentucky
September 30, 1862

Dear Darla,

I thought when I came to these parts if I heard Dixie or the Bonnie Blue Flag one more time that alone would be worth killing a Rebel. Now that the time has passed, I find I have changed my mind.

Darla, I'm going to come straight to the point. I won't be coming back home. I have found another—an acquaintance at first, but it has ripened into love. I am torn at the prospect of breaking your heart, but I find I cannot tear myself away from this place or the woman who nursed me back to health after my arm was shot off. I can only beg your forgiveness and pray that you will find happiness with another who will blot out the pain I cause you now.

It is to my great relief that we did not marry before I left to join the army. I know you will forget me soon enough.

You may be comforted to hear that Gettysburg appears to be well out of range of any prospects for fighting. You should be safe there. The war will be fought on southern soil mainly.

I wish you well,
Goodbye,
Jim

Atlanta, Georgia
September 4, 1862

My dear Elijah,

The house slaves are all we have left. The field hands have all run off. So, there's no one left to take care of the cotton and the livestock. The children make do, helping in a variety of ways. Sarah sews and mends; Reese cooks; Harrison feeds the chickens, collects the eggs and has tried to trap a rabbit or two without much to show for it.

The baby is about to come into this world, such as it is. If it's a boy, I will name him after our fathers as you asked. I hope he has your handsome features and good sense. If it is another girl I shall name her Marietta after our home here. Her name may be all we have left of this place. I have a terrible foreboding. Even so, all I have to give is life force, milk, my arms. Everything else is lacking. Only with you do I have any strength or fight.

When is this madness going to be over? I hope it's only a few months at least—I can't imagine this foolishness will last more than a year.

I bow to your sense of honor and duty and our glorious cause, which seems to grow less glorious each passing day. Is Jefferson Davis a fool? Our only hope is with our savior, Lee.

I imagine like Jesus at Gethsemane he asks that the yoke be taken from him. Well, the good news is, they'll never take Atlanta! Please come home to me, my darling, as soon as you can.

Your faithful wife,
Lily

September, 1862

Dear Brother,

I caution you straight away—do NOT read this letter to our dear Momma and sisters. Their delicate natures could not stand the vile acts I describe herein.

For days now, our company has been camped outside Louisville where the town is overrun with bawdy houses and low women of such I have never seen. The ease with which the men throw away their good sense at the sight of a lady's bosom and enslave their bodies and souls to debauchery would make you sick at the condition of man. Are we so easily shod of our morals? Is there not a lady of upright and modest virtue in all of Kentucky?

Associated plagues and illnesses of the most disreputable sort are crawling through the camp already bedeviled by lice and dysentery.

I fear it is God's hand in these matters—to allow the Devil a free hand to destroy our armies from everyside. If the men aren't whorin' they're diseased; if they are not diseased, they are drunk; if they are not drinking they are playing cards and gambling every night. One war is enough to fight but I fear we fight on many fronts.

And, alas, I can get no one to bother with my sermons on Sunday. They only seek my service on their deathbed. Whiskey on Friday, dying on Saturday, burying on Sunday. This is my life.

> *Pray for our boys and don't forget me,*
> *Your brother and God's servant,*
> *John-Paul*

September 21, 1862

Dear Father,

I once more take pen in hand to write to answer your letter just received. I was glad to get the letter with news about sister and her boys.

If there be any justice in this world, it will do for this misery to end as I do not want sister's boys to grow to an age where this conflict can rob her of them. I am certain, above all things, Mother died of a broken heart worrying about me. I grieve daily.

We are attempting to go to Frankfort to meet the enemy and engage them in due time. Our regiment is lacking water and the sky offers no hope for rain. The land is as dry and cracked as an old man's feet.

Despite this drought, I am well. Please keep me in your prayers. We've been following the Wilderness Road for a time, coming up on a river called the Chaplin. Flows north. I take that as a good sign—a river flowing north. There's peace knowing I'm on the right side of things. History will judge but I know I'm right. My children will talk about this war and our part in it. "The righteous shall inherit the land."

Your loving son,

Joshua

September, 1862

Mrs. Lincoln,

I am ruined—my life is completely turned upside down.

My two sons are dead. My home is burned and I have no husband or help.

Where is your oldest? Safe in some New England school? Not shot through the head lying dead at Shiloh?

What about your husband?
What about your home?
You have other sons and I have none.

My life is over!
I curse you.

May your sons be lost to you.
May your husband as well.
May your days end in horror
May you go straight to Hell.

May your seed never spread. As my loved ones have been blotted from this world, so yours too.

A Southern Patriot

(Note: The envelope containing the following letter was found with directions to the infamous "Bell's Tavern" scribbled on it, surrounded by dark stain. DNA analysis confirmed human blood splatter on the envelope.)

August 29, 1862

My Dearest Frances,

The country in these parts is pretty rough. And I don't mean the land. I mean her people. No one here seems to know the distance from one place to another. It is likely to be ten miles as two. Most don't seem to know what day of the week it is, nor care. They eat with their hands and I haven't run across one who could read a newspaper. This is the most ignorant country a man could ever set foot in.

And that isn't all. Women dip! And spit as well as any man. A site so revolting you have never seen! It has turned me off chew forever. I will never pick up tobacco again as long as I live.

Further, the children smoke and what's worse, swear. Your ears would fall off your head to hear the vile speech coming out of the mouths of little babes.

If this is how it is in the South then they are destined to fall. This is God's divine plan. The North will vanquish an ignorant South to His Glory. It must be manifestly so. God did not intend for this Promised Land to be run by fools—it is our duty to save them from themselves.

Your devoted brother,
Franklin

September 2, 1862

Dear Earl,

We are camped above a pasture of the prettiest land a painter could ever see. I don't expect a more beautiful picture ever hung on a wall that is the view before my eyes now. This Kentucky is near about the most beautiful place I have ever seen or heard tell about.

Despite the drought they've had here for some months now, the corn is high and hay too. I ain't seen one skinny farm animal, or person either. If I believe what my eyes tell me, the war has worked no hardship on the folks here.

I started this letter two days ago. We were in Tennessee after leaving Georgia in the dark of night. The Captain said McCook is on our tail. We run when we have to, eat when we can, sleep in fits and starts.

This war's got everybody so jumpy and nervous a man won't get food or sleep till one side claims a victory.

This is not how I thought I would pass my youth. I want to come home. I miss Mother, and you.

Your devoted brother,
Sam

P.S.

Something's in the water here. I've had the best whiskey I've ever tasted and you would not believe the horses. I may pull up roots and settle here.

The Oaks, Roanoke, VA
September 6, 1862

Dear Son,

I write in great haste. We are ruined. Our place was burned nearly to the ground—and not by armies but by marauding negroes. Our own house workers tried in vain to protect us—and they are with us now—Nellie, Stella, Blind Paw and Miss Cora. We are at The Oaks under the protection of Col. Wainright.

Here is my sad news. Your enfeebled father, unable to travel, will stay here protected by God's grace and the Colonel's sons. Your brothers and sisters, all well, depart with me next week from a prearranged port on the Outer Banks. It will take us days to get there so we have to leave today.

We go to London, England, where your Aunt Doris is expecting us. A letter came months ago begging us to come. I sent word to her that we are on our way. She should receive it in 4 weeks' time—several weeks ahead of our arrival.

Please protect yourself at all costs. I do not want you to make a show of bravery. I want you to be cautious. We are reconciled to this new future and hope that you will join us in our new lives in a more civilized country. Our life here is a shadow. I am afraid the South will never see the sun again.

Enclosed is money for you to come as soon as you can. Write to Mrs. Doris Keppel, King's Row, London W2. It is Union money—as I am not confident confederate money will be worth anything in due course. Please hurry to us. Your father insisted we leave. He knows his days are few. He wanted us to be safe. I could not argue.

Your loving, Mother

P.S.

    I am setting our slaves free once we get to North Carolina. I have never cared for the institution, as you know. America should have heeded Wilberforce and gone the way of England. Alas, we wouldn't be in this mess.

Long Island, NY
May 14, 1862

Dear Father,

I am sitting here finishing up the knitting of these socks for your feet, trying to hurry so I can get this letter to the post. I have been keeping my hands busy so I will not worry myself too much about you, or your health, or to try to figure out where in the world you are right now. I hope when you open this letter, forever after you keep it and all our letters to you close to your heart until we see you again.

Mother reads her Bible daily and I find it an occupation that suits her during these trials. She has grown more slight each passing day, fallin' off to such a degree that she has almost disappeared. She worries too much about you and Rick. Elizabeth has been helping with the knitting, although she mainly holds the woolen thread as I think she is still too young to get the hang of knitting needles yet. When she tires of that I have her help me in the garden.

We say our prayers for you and Rick every morning and night and I know Mother prays for you both continually, without ceasing, during all hours she is awake. Our lives are spent reading newspapers and listening to rumor after rumor after rumor. This place is full of them. I expect the same is true of every little town and village in America. Wars and rumors of war as Revelation says. Do you think we are in the Last Days?

Please know that I am doing my best to care for Mother and Elizabeth. We are doing our best praying for you and Rick. As your daughter, and as a child of God, when I pray, I pray that you both come back again, as God wills it. I say this to you because I know you will understand, being a preacher's daughter. My faith is in Him.

Your faithful daughter,

Lauren

(This envelope was addressed to Mrs. Mary Buddington Gates, Plymouth, MA) September 4, 1862

Dear Mary,

I wanted to write you before we set out toward Kentucky. We are set to meet up with McCook. I don't look forward to crossing the West Virginia mountains we are headed for. They are filled with Southern scum such as they are and I do want to kill my fair share of them. These mountains are rough stuff,

Hell's Gate as I live and breathe… Worse still, these West Virginians are known for their skill with a rifle and being able to melt into the forest as if they are ghosts. Everyone is spooked for sure.

Send food 'cause the food here ain't fit to eat. I ate grits the other day and I can tell you for sure it's what we feed our hogs! Southern food is not fit for human consumption. On top of everything else, the cook is a drunkerd and the officers families get the choicest lots before we get our share. I'm about starved to death. What I wouldn't give for a lobster roll and fresh clams.

My clothes are falling off. I got so many holes in my britches I lost my modesty back in Pennsylvania! Could you send me socks and underwear? A spit of tobacco and some playing cards too.

Sure do wish I was back home. It is pretty country here but looking at a mountain and marching through them is a different thing altogether. I haven't been shot and the only thing I got to show for my troubles so far is a bare backside covered with chigger bites. I have scratched myself raw.

40

I say, if this is the south, give it to 'em. Let 'em have it. No thinking person in their right mind could ever want to live here willingly. Let them and their darkies have it. Sonsofbitches, all of 'em.

Your brother,

John

(Letter postmarked to Mrs. Shepherd Averitt, Sunday Branch Farm, Saratoga, NY) August 31, 1862

Dear Mother,

It is hard to believe it has been a little over a year since we received our colors on the Parade Ground. Following our Standard since has proved to be a lot harder than I had foreseen those many months ago.

We are headed for Kentucky where we are apt to meet the enemy. Our Captain says we are tracking Gen. Bragg's armies. Their intentions are to claim Kentucky for the South. Old Abe would surely roll over and die as have that happen.

My heart is not in the fight. I admit to being afraid, which I pray will make me a cautious man and hopefully keep me alive.

A lot of our boys are hot for a fight. Guess they just want the contest to be decided so they can get back to their lives. Same for me, truth be told.

I do not want to give up, or be disgraced, but some nights I think on how easy it would be to slip away and find my way home.

But I will do a soldier's duty. My sword is for the North and Glory. So be it. Pray for me.

Your son who loves you,
Tommy

(This letter was found among a bundle of letters stamped "Atlanta, Georgia". Microscopic examination found the DNA of domestic pig in the pulp of the paper.)

September 1, 1862

Dear Pa,

Harry, George, and me are still here with the living. God in his infinite wisdom has seen fit to keep us here with Ma and the girls, though the Home Guard come around pretty regular now. Because of that, we have taken to hiding in the hills near Marietta. We get home every few days to check on everyone. We do not know how much longer we will be successful. Harry and George both are scared to death to fight. And I want to join you. The little boys have a hard time between Mother's tears and the casualty lists she carries around with her most every day. Our sisters seem to bear up well for Ma's sake, but she does not appear well. We are greatly afraid her mind is not strong enough to shake the fear of bad news about you. If God is just, He will preserve you for her sake. In the meantime, I do my best to keep up a brave front.

The enemy is not here. Our fear isn't Yankees. It's the raiders, and the Home Guards, and deserters on their way back home. There's lots of movement in these woods at night—we can hear people traveling in small groups. We stay out of harm's way because we don't know who is out there in the dark of night—if they be friend or foe.

I pray for your safe return. It would help to have some money—whatever you can spare. The livestock is all gone with this last hog we butchered just before you left. The corn and what little we have isn't going to last much longer. We try to hunt—but don't want to use up our mini balls—we've got to keep our ammunition and anyway, the blast from the rifles will bring attention and that's the last thing we want. We've been so spoiled by hunting with guns though it's hard to trap anymore. But maybe we'll get better at it. Necessity has a way of improving our skills. Starving too. Don't want you to worry though. We're healthy and alert and ever vigilant about Mother and sisters.

May God keep you safe,
Your loving sons,
Harry, George, and Adam

(Addressee: Mr. Thomas D. Alexander, Richmond, VA)

September 6, 1862

Dear Pa,

We have marched for two weeks straight through without so much as a fare thee well from our commanding officer. And I believe all we've done is go around in circles and have yet to engage the enemy. I have not heard one rifle shot, cannon or bugle blast save our own since I enlisted. I begin to fear this is a war fought in the newspapers only.

The food is god awful, the rations few, the men dirty and the mail is slow. I can suffer the food and a few smelly old soldiers, but the slow mail isn't to be tolerated. My hopes and desires all hang on words from home. Please tell my sisters to write their poor old brother.

The best news it that I am safe as God has obviously seen fit to put me under the command of the sorriest lot in the CSA. At least a skirmish would be nice. I'd rather not die of shame, but with honor and in a hero's grave. This war is nothing.

Your son,

Joe

P.S.

That fool, James Smith, I wrote you about—the boy from Roanoke—he blew off his own toe with his pistol. Waste of a bullet if you ask me.

Mrs. Mary Margaret Woodward
Jackson, MS
September 2, 1862

Dearest Mother,

I am shot in the left leg. I am afraid the doctor wants to cut it off. I have begged him to leave it on. He says it can't wait but I do not want to be a cripple.

Ma! Good news! My leg is saved. I started this letter three days ago and had the devil of a time telling the doc that I was going to keep my leg. I have gone through the worst of it and it appears to be better. The doc did set the bones and he says I should stay off it for three to six months. So, here is the best part—I am coming home on sick leave until the end of December at least! Now I just need to find a way home.

I know you have been praying for me all along. And even though you can't know about my leg, I feel sure God has placed this burden on your heart and even though you didn't know it, you were praying for me to get through whatever trials I have been burdened with. I have sat next to you in church and heard your prayers enough to know what you would pray and I know this to be true. How else could my leg be saved and God send me home besides? You always did say prayers was the strongest force in the universe and I'm now a believer.

To that end, I want to say that I have been thinking a lot lately on these mysteries and therefore have decided that when I get home I want to be baptized in the river and dedicate my life to Jesus. For surely He is good and merciful. My tent mate is a boy name Graham who's always got a Bible story and talks to me about the Bible in a way that's new. I think he has a future in the church. I think I may follow his way.

Your loving son,
Gabe

Richmond, KY
September 8, 1862

Dearest Father,

I am shot. A kind nurse writes for me. Snipers bushwacked us while we were headed for Camp Nelson. It doesn't look good. Please tell Mother that I love her and for her to know that we will meet again at The Rapture where we will go to Glory together. When next I see you, we will be in Heaven together. I am proud of our country and hope Mr. Lincoln stays with it. I am not suffering so do not feel bad on that account. The doctor had something to give me for the pain—it makes me want to sleep. Which is how I expect we all want to leave this earth when our time is done.

I am proud to be your son. I am proud to have served my country. Do not weep for me for I go to sleep and wait to see Paradise with you all soon. If God takes me up sooner, I will watch over you all from my heavenly seat.

Your devoted son,
Andrew

Enclosed letter:

Dear Sir: Your son died on September 9, 1862. He had a Christian burial at the Camp Nelson cemetery, with full military honors. Enclosed is his Bible, a locket he said belonged to his mother, and his pipe. Our deepest condolences on the death of a gallant soldier and child of God.

Sincerely,
Joel Egerton, MD Camp Nelson,
KY

Charleston, So. Carolina
August 27, 1862

Dear Son,

If ever a Mother's prayers were answered it was yesterday when at last, I received your letters. From the look of them, they were pretty worn and dirty. They had seen a lot on their journey here. Was it rain or tears that fell on some pages you wrote, my son? I have slept with them clutched to my heart through the night.

I cannot believe you are so far away—in enemy lands where the cold fall nights will set in before long. I send along two pairs of britches, a cotton set of drawers, four pairs of socks, some coffee, and more paper and pen.

That your regiment is heading for Kentucky is concerning. That's Lincoln land! May God Have Mercy.

Don't try to be brave. Save yourself at all costs and whatever safe refuge God gives you. Keep your head down and stay alert.

The corn is high and the melons and tomatoes are ripening on the vine. All our negroes have not abandoned us yet, though some have taken their leave. Your father and I gave them what we could spare. We are afraid the freedom they seek will come at a high price. At least here they had a roof over their heads and plenty to eat and their families were all together. We have never been cruel. How I wish we would have had the courage to set all our slaves free. God is going to judge us harshly for our part in this lamentable history. Maybe this is His judgment. This whole cause is a confusion that won't be reconciled by a war I can tell you. It has to come from within men's hearts—it cannot be forced. It isn't a matter of if, but when, my son. We are on the wrong side, I tell you. And our children's children will be held to account. I am sorry for all of us.

I long to see you, love,

Mama

(This letter was remarkable for the large bills of Confederate money found inside, which have been turned over to the Battle of Perryville Museum.)

September 1, 1862

Dear Alexander,

Can you do something for me?

We are down here in Atlanta getting ready to ride as far as the trains will take us, headed northwest. I think we're headed to Tennessee or Kentucky. All that time in cramped, close quarters on a train can only mean one thing—fights!

My men are hungry, shoeless, and clothed in rags. The rations are so pitiful I can't help but predict a demise of many due to starvation. More will die an ignominious death than on the glorious field of battle.

Please go to Kathy and tell her I said to give you whatever we have in our stores, save what she needs for three months. I need clothes, shoes, minnie balls, powder, pen, ink, socks, underwear, salt pork, whatever has been put up, flour, and cornmeal. If one more soldier eats hard tack, there will be another rebellion the likes of which the southern and northern armies have never seen. Get me all the whiskey you can, and Lord God above, all things tobacco and coffee—real coffee. There'll be a big reward. Ship as soon as you can. Enclosed is some money.

Your devoted brother,

Julian

Nashville, TN
August 14, 1862

Dear Elias,

You have been found out!

You better hope you meet your maker on the battlefields of Kentucky, because if you set foot back inTennessee, your ass is mine.

I found my three coon dogs in your barn. You are the lowest form of earth scum. I will take the hide off you if you show your face in these parts.

I curse you to hell.

And by the way, according to your wife, I am the best lover she's ever had...well, at least good enough that I got that crazy bitch to confess about my dogs.

You took my three bitches, so I took your one!

May you burn in hell,
Martin Van Buren McCoy

Nashville, TN
August 8, 1862

My dearest husband,
Destroy after reading...
I am WILD as a buck. And I can't get no relief! I stay awake nights tossing and turning and nearly drive myself crazy needing you so badly. This little doodad of a finger don't begin to measure up to your manliness. I can't get no satisfaction.

Here's some gossip: There is a rumor that many of the younger women in these parts are resorting to measures...in the form of OTHER MEN! Your wife may be nothing more than a needy woman but you can rest assured I will NEVER resort to whoring myself out for satisfaction or money—and that's the second rumor—seems like a lot of women are resorting to whoring for money 'cause times are so hard.

I'm positively beside myself. It is not fair that a woman of my age should have to go without her husband in the fullness of her youth.

Oh, this war is cruel indeed.

The only relief I am getting is riding. I hate to confess but the horse seems to flinch when he sees me. I've rode him so hard lately I'm sure he's got saddle sores—but it's the only satisfaction I'm getting!

I'll be glad when you get home so I can ride you!

> *Your desperate but loving wife,*
> *Liza*

Cairo, Illinois
July 8, 1862

Dear Cletus,

Your family anxiously awaits word from you. Where are you? We have heard you are in headed to Kentucky. Rumors are flying that General Buell aims to get the state for Abe. One can only hope.

I have some news that makes me blush at the very prospect at putting it down on paper. Your sister, Hildegard, is with child! Your father is about out of his mind with rage and that awful boy who was sniffing around her has "run off", according to his family, but we just discovered he apparently enlisted and is in the same unit as you—the 24th Illinois!

Can you find him? His name is Ernest Meath. They say he is in Company E. I do believe your father will come to Kentucky himself to find him and kill him. There are other solutions, of course. You could approach him and give him the choice of returning with the promise of marriage?

I expect, knowing his sort and the family he comes from, he will deny his paternity. In which case I'm sure you will find other recourse, if you get my meaning. We need your father here with us.

I am sorry to be the bearer of such news.

Your loving Auntie,
Athalia

Bardstown, KY
September 27, 1862

Dear Mr. and Mrs. Meath,

It is with deep regret that I write to inform you of the death of your son, Ernest Meath. While he was eager in all things and heartily showed this Company the type of man he was, unfortunately he did not die a hero's death upon the battlefield.

An accident occurred yesterday while the men were cleaning their rifles and as many ways as God's ways are mysterious, so too was his untimely death. It seems he must have tripped on his gun as he was preparing to clean it and for reasons we cannot explain, the gun exploded, killing him instantly. That is our only consolation, that he did not suffer. His death was quick.

On another note, perhaps of more sorrow or relief, I enclose herewith a letter from him to Hildegard.

Your obt. Servant,
Captain Ulrich Ghent

June 4, 1862

Dear Hildegard,

I did not mean to leave so suddenly when last we met. We were found out and my father took me to the army headquarters and signed me up that very next morning just as the soldiers were leaving.

Although, I suspect the real reason I'm here is because my family needed the money I'd earn being a soldier. I am glad we Hand-Fasted in the Irish way before I left, in case I don't come back. You keep this letter to show we are legitimately married.

What I really want is for us to start a life together. Please wait for me. I'll be home soon.

Your loving,
Ernest

September 16

Dear Adolph,

Your eldest son, Adolph Jr., was out squirrel hunting yesterday and shot himself! He was out with two other boys and up to mischief no doubt, which, by the way, he gets from you. I learned they was squirrel hunting in town—right outside the house of that Hildegard girl. So what kind of squirrel hunting do you suppose those boys was up to? She has a suspect reputation. I heard a rumor she was pregnant.

Squirrel hunting as I know it and the kind them boys was up to don't bear no resemblance. How come Adolph Jr. got so much of you and so little of me? Besides, everybody knows he couldn't hit an elephant out of a tree. Right now, he's laid up with a clean shot through the shoulder. We was able to tidy him up real good. The boy is going to be fine.

In the meantime, I miss you something fierce. It's hell being the mother of all these boys without you around to help me. Their little peckers are all they think about. Again, like you!

Come home, my love!
Nell

Nashville, TN
September 3, 1862

My dear Daniel,

I read the papers and have been trying to follow your location. I expect you are getting ready to be in the thick of it up there in Abe Lincoln territory. But on balance, it is also the truth that our own president is also a native son of Kentucky. I'd feel a sight better if he was from South Carolina, a state that knows its side of things—affairs being so conflicted North and South, East and West, Slave and Free, Black and White. Well, it's a wonder any of us knows who we are and what we are about.

My only aim is for you to keep your head down. Don't be reckless with your life; don't take chances.

If you get winged, don't you worry about it. I'd rather have you in parts than not at all. And if, God forbid, your time on this earth is done, I'll come find you and bring you home and put you next to Ophelia down by the creek. S h e sure was a good dog. But, on that note, I've got a surprise waiting for you. I call her Little Ophelia, she's not as big as our beautiful Ophelia but looks exactly like her. I figured you'd be needing a new coon dog when you get back home. I wanted you to have something to look forward to.

Your wife is busy with your children. They stay busy with chores. I stay in my rocker, worrying. At my age all I can do is take on the concerns of this world and pray God ends this conflict soon—so I rock and pray and rock and worry.

I have sent along some socks as winter is coming.   Do not fear.   God has told me that He will let me see you again.

I love you, my dearest boy,

Mother

August 17, 1862
Nashville, TN

Dear Captain Murray,

I beg your pardon to interrupt your very important war business to ask a very large favor to soothe a mother's worries.

Can you send my son home for a short spell? His name is Elias Womack. We have troubles here and I am afraid the war battles you're fighting in Kentucky ain't nuthin' compared to what's fixin' to blow up here in Nashville.

There's a boy here, Martin Van Buren McCoy, who is going to steal my son's coon dogs. He's already sleeping with his wife. Well, she's gone to whorin' and I don't really care about that. She was trash anyway, but I do care if Mr. McCoy comes here and starts a fight over the dogs. You see, my husband, Mr. Womack, believes the dogs belong to him as my son told him he got 'em off a guy who was kilt at Shiloh and then my son gave him to his Pa for his birthday.

Between my husband, Martin, Elias' wife, and now the dogs, I am afraid that the trouble about to start here will necessitate that my son return home. His father, my husband, Mr. Womack, only has one leg. I know you will ask what does a one-legged man have any business with all those coon dogs? Well, he raises 'em to sell. I have another son, Doodle, who can come and take Elias' place. I won't wait for an answer. Doodle is on his way. I trust you will honor this request as I am about wore out from worry.

A faithful Southern lady,
Mrs. Carole Dechman Womack

August 15, 1862
Nashville, TN

Dear Joe,

Are you in the same Company as Elias? If you are, be prepared for some fireworks in your camp.

Martin McCoy found his dogs in Mr. Womack's barn. Martin was so mad it took us a week just to calm him down. He has sworn an oath to see Elias in Hell.

Well, we could hardly imagine how he could do much harm to Elias, seeing as how he's enlisted and probably marching to Kentucky, from what we hear down here. But, by God, it looks like Martin was good on his word. He's gone and had his way with Elias' wife. I think there was something cookin' in the kitchen between them two before Elias left. You know that old sayin' where there's smoke there's fire. Of course, she ain't been turnin' away no takers since Elias left—truth be told. Sadly, there's lots of our women who have been resorting to money making schemes of a disreputable nature since the war started, if you get my drift. But, according to Martin, it was during his "visit" with Elias' wife that she spilled the beans about Martin's coon dogs.

You better watch out for Elias. He's dumb as a board. But his heart ain't evil. I'm afraid the news about the wife will hurt. It might cause him to be preoccupied and I'm afraid he won't keep his guard up. Many a man has lost his life when he's worryin' 'bout troubles back home.

So, keep an eye out.

Your servant in Christ,
Brother Matthew

September 19, 1862
Cairo, Illinois

Dear Louis,

I heard a rumor that your wife is pregnant, again! I heard another rumor that you stay in regular contact with her—at least a letter every two weeks. I have gotten one letter from you since you enlisted. One! And you told me that relations with your wife stopped when you met me six months ago. I can add. Can you?

You better hope that child comes out lookin' like a Chinaman or your wife will be getting a letter from me. I'm sure she will be shocked to find the letter you wrote me and the drawing of yourself AND the many descriptions of the ways you'd like to have me. Or maybe I'll just send it to her right now?

If this baby is yours, you better hope a confederate kills you 'cause your life back here won't be worth coming back to.

I mean it!
Kate

Cairo, Illinois
September 16, 1862

My darling,

I am so lonesome without you. Things are very quiet here as you can probably imagine—what with all the able-bodied men in five counties somewhere in Kentucky right now.

When all you boys signed up, business really fell off, if you know what I mean. I've had to resort to honest work and I can tell you ironing and cleaning don't much suit my tastes. I sure will be glad when this war business is over.

Personally, it don't make much difference to me which side wins. Me bein' a woman means I'm still at the mercy of men—white or black, free or slave, North or South. So, the way I see it, I expect to make my way in this world—and my fortune—the best way I know how. In the arms of anyone who can pay the price, dressed up in the finest silks my ill-gotten gains can buy and perched on top of the plushest couch north of the Ohio River.

But I have to admit, I do have my favorites and you are at the top of the list. When you get back, your first poke is free!

I miss you, you old goat!
Nora

Cairo, Illinois
August 2, 1862

Dear Will,

Remember that night down by the creek? Remember what you said, "Don't worry, nothing's going to happen?"

Well, something has happened and in about 6 months, it will be born and bear a great likeness to you I am sure.

My sister has written to my brother, Hank, remember him? The big blonde from the Mother country? He is also in the 24th Illinois. I am sure that he will be trying to find you soon.

Also, just in case, my father is on his way to Kentucky. You don't have to worry about getting killed by a confederate. Your fate is going to be much worse. You've lied to me, spawned a child, and now your fate won't be an honorable one. I'd be lookin' over my shoulder if I was you.

I may have been only 12, but I told you I was a bleeder! Enjoy your last days, death rides a fast horse.

You can rot in hell,

Angel

Nashville, TN
September 22, 1862

Dear Isaiah,

Your sister, Ruth, has been captured by the Union Army. They are holding her as a spy. Word has it that she was consorting with the officers in a bawdy house. They say she got drunk one night and when an officer got too fresh, she pulled out a knife, held it to his throat, said she'd rather kill a Yankee than "F___" one. So, she's in the stockade and the whole city is on fire with the news.

Who knew Ruth had such spirit? The boys in gray should call her Saint Ruth. I expect they will soon enough. She's supposed to hang tomorrow. Sorry to break the news, but you should be proud of your sister.

Your friend,
Joe

Nashville, TN
August 14, 1862

Dear Doc,

Have you heard the news from your brother, Pleasant? His family is ruined. The bank foreclosed on their home. His wife and children moved in with her parents.

Unless things change soon—unless this war is over soon, I am afraid we are destined to meet the same fate. What do you want me to do?

Things are unraveling quickly here. Many of our very finest families have fallen on hard times. Several women have taken in boarders but rumor has it that's not all they're doing—understand what I'm saying? A lady's virtue can be bought dirt cheap in these parts. Mine is not for sale.

I'm with Doris on that score. Damn the house—the bank can have it—we'll get another one. But I'll not sell one inch of my flesh for the sake of a few old boards and rusty nails. But I would like your advice just the same. I guess if Lot's daughters sinned, I could too, but only with your blessing.

I love you,
Clarissa

Kansas City, Kansas
August 1, 1862

Dear Mr. Byars,

I wanted to inform you that your wife, Janet, has been imprisoned in the County Jail for the past week with a charge of prostitution. And, to make matters worse, rumor has it she kept records which indicate in the month of July, your wife was in receipt of $300 paid in gold for services rendered. There is no judgment here, but one wonders when she found time for sleep.

Which brings me to the matter of your children. They are now wards of the state and have been sent to an orphanage in Louisville.

I hope you are able to get leave so you can come back to Kentucky and attend to these matters.

I know you to be a man of honor. A lot of our Southern women have traded theirs to feed their children. Do not blame her. Blame Lincoln.

A sympathizer.

Dear Tilghman,

It is your Aunt Agnes.

My dear boy, I have had one of my visions and I'm afraid the news is not good. I saw you being carried off by winged doves into the clouds.

Pray your end is quick and make your peace with God.

You have been a good nephew. I will see that you are buried next to your Pa and Ma.

You made me promise when you left that if I saw anything, I was not to hold back. I am keeping my promise to you so that you can sanctify your thoughts and body. The Bible says Blessed are the Peacemakers—Your reward is to get out of this hell on earth and you will see your parents soon.

We, too, shall meet again on that glorious avenue.

I have loved you like my own son,

Aunt Agnes

Paducah, KY
September 8, 1862

Dear Robert,

The first few weeks out on march, I was horny. But that wore off soon enough as I was too tired to be horny; then that became a faint memory as I am now about starved to death.

When I joined up, it was for the uniform, to see new places and to be kissed by pretty girls. To be a hero.

Now I ain't nothin' but a fool and a damned one at that.

I was on sentry post last night and after finally getting some good rations—rabbit and real bread—I no sooner finished eating than got a little spirit up, if'n you know what I mean. I took care of that and must have fallen fast asleep.

They are hangin' me tomorrow for shirking my duty—apparently, 20 of our best horses were stolen in the night—we think it was Indians—but I'm the one who will pay.

Anyway, like I said, they're hanging me tomorrow. Please do not give Ma the particulars. Makeup something good. I guess this is one time I'm thankful she can't read. After you have read this, please make up one of your good yarns and tell her I died a hero in a skirmish.

I am done for.

Till we meet again,
Jed

Chattanooga, Tennessee
May 14, 1862

Dear Sir,

I am in receipt of your letter of May 13th.

When you were home on leave and called on me and my sisters at Beau Voir, we were pleased to accept your acquaintance based on the recommendation of our cousin, Mr. Charles Walker, whose letter you had in your possession.

When we invited you to the charity ball in support of our great cause, we did so due to your gallant work offshore and that business about the merchant ship of which our cousin so highly praised you in his letter of introduction.

When we had you and your sister to dine, we were likewise charmed by her grace and poise. Alas, sir, we have found you out!

Our cousin denies all knowledge of you.

You have been revealed to be a pirate and worse yet, your "sister" runs a bawdy house. You, sir, are no gentleman.

Please refrain from all future correspondence nor show yourself within five counties of BeauVoir or you will be held to account for your unsavory, unseemly, and ungallant behavior.

No doubt but you are a Yankee spy!

Utterly sincerely,
Three Confederate ladies

Birmingham, Alabama
September 2, 1862

Dearest,

Where are you, my love? Under what starry sky do you sleep tonight? Is it as pretty as the stars above our home in Alabama?

Is the owl watching over you? The moon lighting your way? Do the crickets' chorus herald your advance? Or grow silent in awe at the coming of the mighty army?

If I were a bird, I'd fly my way to you. I'd screech out a warning when the enemy approaches. I'd soar above your march to lead the way to safety. I'd sing you to sleep at night and make a cheerfulsong to wake you. You could follow my melody all the way back to me.

Come back safe to me, my love.

Your nest is soft and warm, and
ready,
Elmira

P.S.

Here is a locket with my hair and likeness—wear it next to your heart.

(A locket with a faded portrait of a young woman was found among the dead on the battlefield. Could this be Elmira's? The locket is in a cabinet in the Perryville Battlefield Museum among other items, to include: several rosaries, a brass snuffbox, a ladies' fan, a ladies' handkerchief, intricately carved bone writing pens, leather money pouches, a man's engraved gold watch, glasses, etc.)

October 7, 1862
Frankfort, KY

September 9, 1862

Dear Family,

   I have but a few minutes to write to you before daybreak.

   Today we've had a place to rest and pick blackberries and search for water. There is a terrible drought in Kentucky. The boys break ranks every chance they get to find water and won't heed any order. A man's thirst takes priority over a general's command.

   I want this business to be done so I can get home to you all. The talk is that this campaign will be over by Christmas and the enemy whipped. God make it so.

   Please do not worry about my arm. The surgeon said it will be crooked which is a sight better than no arm at all. The good news about falling off that horse was that I will not be seeing any action at the campaign somewhere near the Chaplin River. There is a little town called Perryville nearby. I am to help out with the supplies and make myself useful writing letters for the soldiers.

   Pray for victory to come quick as I am awful anxious to get home.

   Hopefully, this impending battle will be the mother of all battles and be talked about through the ages as the battle that won the war and our country can be reunited. I fear the alternative—that it will be just another battle in a long war stretching out into a future we cannot cast our eyes upon because of the sorrow it will unleash and the devastation it will leave in its wake. I fear the effects of this war will be felt throughout succeeding generations. While our children's children may not be responsible for our mistakes, they will have to deal with the results of what we do here now for generations.

Exodus 34:7

So, for all your hopes and dreams and wishes to be so, pray without ceasing that these two armies meeting up soon somewhere in the middle of Kentucky will be the beginning of the end and I will be heading home in a few days' time.

God's Love Cover You,

Your faithful son and brother,
Augustus James

* * *

In Closing

The Battle of Perryville, also known as the Battle of the Chaplin Hills, was fought on October 8, 1862. Led by General Braxton Bragg of the Confederate Army and General Don Carlos Buell's Union Army, the battle was a tactical win for the South. Even so, the South was outnumbered.

Retreating, Kentucky was therefore in Union hands.

Perryville was the second bloodiest battle in the western theater after Shiloh as of 1862.

Cleo Woodward was my maternal great-grandmother and daughter-in-law of Alexander McRae Dechman, my great-great grandfather and the founder of Grand Prairie, Texas. While he was in the Texas calvary he met Robert E. Lee and years later he left behind his impression of Lee in a brief history of his life. His eldest son, my great-grandfather, Thomas Morgan Dechman, was stolen by Indians and returned unharmed.

I would like to thank my husband, Tom, for his steadfast love, constant devotion, and unwavering enthusiasm for this project. Like the good professor that he is, he gave me criticism and encouragement.